When Mary saw her look so sad, | She went to her, and kindly said,
And lean against the tree, | "Do come and play with me."

Original frontispiece from 1849 printing

COUSIN ANN'S
STORIES FOR CHILDREN

By Ann Preston

Edited, with a
New Introduction by

Richard Beards, Ph.D.

With New Illustrations &
Design by

Stevie French

Inner Light Books
San Francisco, California

Edited by Richard Beards
rbeardsbookplace@gmail.com
All art and design by Stevie French,
www.steviefrench.com

Published by Inner Light Books
San Francisco, California
Please visit us on the Web at
www.innerlightbooks.com
editor@innerlightbooks.com

Library of Congress Control Number: 2010941820

ISBN 978-0-9797110-8-4 (hardcover)
ISBN 978-0-9797110-9-1 (paperback)

INTRODUCTION.

Ann Preston (1813-1872) is best known as a medical pioneer and nineteenth century Quaker activist. She was the first woman Dean of the Women's Medical College of Pennsylvania (1866), a graduate of its initial class (1851), Professor of Physiology and Hygiene (1853) and founder and director of the Womens's Hospital of Philadelphia (1862). A birthright Quaker, daughter of Amos and Margaret Smith Preston of West Grove, Chester County, Pennsylvania, Ann Preston was a member of the Clarkson Antislavery Society, an advocate of temperance and a teacher, both of her six surviving brothers and other local children in the 1830's and 1840's. During this time, she was surrogate housewife and mother in her own family because her mother was failing rapidly, dying in 1848.

Ann Preston undoubtedly benefited from the local lyceum, which had among its speakers James Russell Lowell and the Quaker poet John Greenleaf Whittier, the local public library, a literary society and a local anti-slavery society of which she was the secretary. At this period, the late 1830's, Ann is known to have written a poem about the burning of Philadelphia's Pennsylvania Hall in 1838 by an anti-abolition mob. She also composed "The Child's Playhouse" in 1842 and "To a Departed Sister" in 1843, while teaching physiology and hygiene to young women, and promoting temperance, anti-slavery, women's rights and anti-capital punishment.

The immediate cause of the publication of *Cousin Ann's Stories for Children* (1849) was probably the recent 27 hour escape at the end of March, 1849, of Henry "Box" Brown, who having lost his family, escaped north in a small wooden crate. It was opened in Philadelphia by members of the Philadelphia Vigilance Committee which included William Still and James Miller McKim. The latter, a Presbyterian minister, ardent abolitionist and editor-manager of The Pennsylvania Freeman became the publisher of *Cousin Ann's Stories for Children*, which includes a two-page story of Brown's escape, the first published account of this slave's journey to freedom. One surmises Ann Preston gathered some previously written poems and short prose pieces and, at McKim's urging, produced the book.

The poems and stories in *Cousin Ann's Stories for Children* feature a number of Ann Preston's lifelong interests. In addition to the story of "Box" Brown, two other stories, "Howard and His Squirrel" and "Tom and Lucy: A Tale for Little Lizzie" discuss enslavement; Howard keeps his squirrel in a cage but decides to set "Bunny the squirrel" free. "But Howard thought he should not like/ a little slave to be. A bird or squirrel in a cage/ It makes me sad to see; It seems so cruel to confine/ The creatures made so free." Immediately after comes "Tom and Lucy" about an African-American brother and sister who first see their parents sold separately, then are themselves consigned to different owners. Lucy ends up picking cotton, and Tom, after a failed escape, is sent to Georgia in chains.

Other poems connect to additional Ann Preston concerns. Three poems deride overindulgence—"Johnny Vanline" starts with cider and becomes alcoholic; "Lola Lake and Lila Lee" contrasts Lila who drinks fresh water and follows a healthy diet to Lola who eats only "candy, nuts, and cake." "I'll Never Use Tobacco" expresses the words of ten year old Robert Reid who sees his friend Jerry start with cigarettes; the reader then follows Jerry's downward spiral as he devolves into the village ne'er do-well. Ann Preston's early interest in hygiene and health is evident in her 1830's talks to young women about their bodies and in her later temperance commitment.

And there are pieces about the natural world. "The Chestnut Hunt" describes the country tradition of whipping chestnut trees with sticks in October to make the nuts fall. The nut gatherers, who include an African American child, cooperate happily, mind five year old Georgy, and think of a present for father should they sell enough chestnuts. In "The Birds," Preston emphasizes the importance of learning the names of species, not just using the generic word "birds." Knowing names acknowledges the variety of God's creation and makes us both closer to and more observant of the birds and their songs, behavior, and habitat. Preston, herself a keen observer of her natural surroundings in her letters to friends, is in the spirit of Quaker botanists and naturalists including the Bartrams, John and William, and Chester County's own Humphry Marshall. Other poems and stories focus on carelessness ("Willy Way"), trustworthiness vs. temptation to theft ("Charles Clear"), and school yard decorum.

Despite her scant formal education prior to medical study—a few years at a Quaker elementary school in West Grove and a brief period in 1830-1831 at a Quaker girls' boarding school in West Chester, PA—Preston always understood the power of learning. In the midst of her medical studies at the Women's Medical College of Pennsylvania, she writes to Hannah Darlington, a close friend and former teacher: "I find my studies as interesting as those we used to pursue at West Grove where thy help made the hard places easy and I pitied Father and Mother because they could not go to school." Ann Preston herself was teaching as an eighteen year old: she writes to Sarah Coates on December 28, 1831 "I have run into the school room to write this; I am teaching a small school at home." Preston's responsibility as the only surviving daughter of three sisters to teach and raise her six younger brothers made her keenly responsive to boyish behavior as well as the temptations facing youth. When her brothers could be on their own, she taught other children, leading to her lectures on hygiene to young women and ultimately her teaching duties at the Women's Medical College. Given this life long commitment, that she produced *Cousin Ann's Stories for Children* cannot come as a surprise. In its address "To My Little Readers" she explains "there are many thousands of you: and I cannot see all your faces, and talk with every one of you though I am far away. I shall be pleased if you learn something good and pleasant from it." What they are to learn—temperance, healthy diet and avoidance of tobacco, to treasure freedom and abhor slavery, the bounty and beauty of God's creation, the need to treat others generously and honestly—these themes and interests were the mainstays of Anne Preston's own life, as student and teacher, as community member and Quaker, as doctor, medical administrator and social activist. Though *Cousin Ann's Stories for Children* is one hundred and sixty-two years old, it still speaks to contemporary concerns and moral perspectives.

Richard Beards, Ph.D.,
Temple University

TO MY LITTLE READERS.

DEAR CHILDREN :
I will tell you how I came to think of making
this little book: I love children, and it would be
pleasant to me to see you, and talk with you about
many things. It is not very long since I was a little
child myself, and played "Blind man's buff," and
"Frog in the Sea," as merrily as any of you. But
there are many thousands of you; and I cannot see
all your faces, and talk with every one of you: so I
thought I would write a little book, and that
would be a good way to speak with you, though I
am far away. I hope you will like it. I shall be
pleased if you learn something good and pleasant
from it. You will soon be men and women, and I
want you to grow wiser and better every day. Then
you will be happy, and God will bless you and keep
you.

–COUSIN ANN.

MARY MAY

Dear Annie, did you ever hear
  About sweet Mary May ?
She hung her satchel on her arm,
  And tripped to school each day.

She beat the Sun, for she got up
  When first the robin sang,
And knew her lessons very well
  Before the school bell rang.

The teacher smiled to see her come,
  With face so bright and gay,
And all the scholars dearly loved
  The loving Mary May.

And then, they said, she played
      at noons
  The very best of all,
At "jump the rope," and "hide and
      whoop,"
  "prisoner's base," and "ball."

She would not cheat at any game,
  Though she were seen by none;
Nor would she pout and quit the
      play,
  Nor scold at any one.

Now Susan Sand went to that school
  And lonely seemed all day,
Her clothes were coarse, and no
      one asked
The friendless girl to play.

When Mary saw her look so sad,
  And lean against the tree,
She went to her and kindly said,
  "Do come and play with me!"

The scholars stared while Mary led
  Poor Susan by the hand;
They said "'tis queer that Mary May
  Will go with Susan Sand!"

But Mary stay'd by Susan's side,
  And played with her each day :
At last the children said " 'Tis right
  To do like Mary May."

And so they played with Susan, too,
  And were a happy band
When, like sweet Mary May,
      they all
  Were kind to Susan Sand.

The same great Father made
      each one,
  Though some are poor and small,
And if our hearts are good
      and kind,
  We, too, will love them all.

THE BIRDS

The lark sits on the tree tops tall,
And sweetly sings till late in fall;
The red bird wears its dress so gay,
And visits us the coldest day.
The wren builds nests in boxes small,
Or in a tree, or on a wall,
And sings a song as loud and clear
As though it wanted all to hear.
On bright March mornings blue birds sing:
The blackbirds take the corn in spring,
But yet they do more good than harm
By taking worms that hurt the farm.
The meadow thrush, with bright, brown wings,
And speckled bosom, gaily sings.
In meadows sweet, on summer days,
"Bob-white," "Bob-white," the partridge says.
Far in the woods, on tree tops tall,
The wood thrush sings most sweet of all.
When night comes down, and all is still,
You'll hear the noisy whip-poor-will,
It says " whip-poor-will," "whip-poor-will."

I knew a boy who used to play
In fresh green fields the whole long day,
And songs from morn till night he heard,
And yet he did not know a bird.
But, Eddy, you must never be
So stupid and so blind as he,
But learn their names, and love them too,
And watch what funny things they do:
Yet spoil no nest, my darling boy,
But let the sweet birds live in joy.

WILLY WAY

"O where's my hat?" cried Willy Way,
  "I never saw the beat,
You always hide my hat away
  Or tramp it with your feet.

"And then, my book I cannot get,—
  That blue book which I own,
I'd thank you if you'd please to let
  My books, and things alone."

So Willy had an angry look,
  And hunted long about,
For he, himself, had dropped
      his book,
  And left his new hat out.

He never put his things away,
  As careful children do,

And so he lost them every day,
  And lost his temper too.

He would not stop to clean his feet,
  But brought in mud from play,
And Hannah, who was very neat,
  Wished he was far away.

To Uncle John's, one morning bright,
  His cousins went to play,
But Uncle John would not invite
  The careless Willy Way:

Aunt Jane, he said, must work
      much more
  When Willy was about,
And Willy must improve before
  He was invited out.

CHARLES CLEAR

Charles Clear was a handsome little boy, with curly hair and dark hazel eyes. But he had something far better than fine looks. "And what could that be?" said little Margaret.

I will tell you: he had a good heart; and so his papa said he was worth more than ten times his weight in gold. When he wanted anything done, he did not say "Tom, bring me my hat;" "Lucy, I want a drink, give it to me;" but he waited upon himself when he could do it; and when he could not, he would say, "will you please to do this for me."

He said he thought it was a shame to live an idle life; and when he was asked to do anything, he never said "I won't," or "let James do it," as idle Timothy Toots would do, but he did it himself, as soon as he could.

One day his mother sent him to carry a basket of nice cakes to a poor woman who lived a mile off. Timothy Toots went with him, and when they got out of sight, Timothy said to Charles, "let us eat some of these nice cakes; there will be enough left for that old woman, and your mamma will never know it." But Charles said, "no, indeed! it would be just as bad as if she did know it. Besides, she has trusted me to carry these cakes, and I would not deceive my mother for all the cakes in the country."

So Timothy felt ashamed, and the poor woman blessed Charles many times, and said, "your mother is very kind." Timothy thought no one would find him out at his sly tricks, but he often got caught, and, at last, nobody could trust him. People would say when they saw him pass by, "there goes a naughty boy that no one can believe." Besides, his own thoughts found him out, and shamed him.

Timothy felt badly; for people who do wrong are always unhappy. I think one reason that Charles Clear acted so well was because he tried to have good thoughts. His mother told him that he must not keep any thoughts in his mind that he would be ashamed for her to know. If any ugly thoughts came, she said he must drive them away, as if they were thieves.

So he thought about his books, and his work, and his pleasant plays, and when any bad thoughts peeped in, there was no room for them, and they soon went away. Now, won't you do like little Charles Clear?

HOWARD and His SQUIRREL

Our Howard had a little squirrel,
Its tail was long and grey,
He put it in a wiry cage,
And there it had to stay.
Its hickory nuts and corn it ate
From out its little paw,
And such a funny, active thing,
I think, I never saw.
But Howard thought he should not like
A little slave to be;
And God had made the nimble squirrel,
To run, and climb the tree.
And so he opened Bunny's door,
And laughed to see it run
And spring right up the leafy tree,
As if 'twas only fun.
A bird or squirrel in a cage
It makes me sad to see;
It seems so cruel to confine
The creatures made so free.

TOM AND LUCY:
A Tale for Little Lizzie

Come Lizzie, and I'll tell that tale
  Of Tom and Lucy Lee,
Two little slaves, no bigger, dear,
  Than cousin Charles and thee.

They lived in Carolina state,
  Beside the great, deep sea;
Their mother was a weary slave
  And wanted to be free.

She only came to them at dark,
  For she must work all day,
And with her, on the cabin floor,
  They slept the night away.

Long sunny days they played alone,
  As little children play,
But never hurt the butterflies,
  Nor pelted frogs away.

Sometimes they rambled in
    the wood,
  Where moss and flowers grew,
And little birds sang them to sleep,
  As birds will often do.

But one dark night their mother dear
  Stayed all the night away,
And long they cried, and waited there,
  Until the break of day;

And then their master came, and bade
  Them to his house repair,
For they were old enough, he said,
  To earn their victuals there:

They met their mother in a drove
  Of slaves, upon their way;
Her heart was broke, for she was sold
  To go to Florida.

She gazed on them and cried
    "My God!"
  She stopped, and begged to stay:
The driver fiercely called "move on,"
  And drove her fast away.

Through dreary days and
    dreary years
  Toiled Tom and Lucy there,
And when they stopped, the great
    whip cracked
  Upon their shoulders bare.

But though they'd none to
    pity them,
They loved each other well,
And love will always bring
    some joy,
Wherever it may dwell.

They said when they grew big
    and strong
They both would run away,
And, up in Pennsylvania, learn
    To read and write, each day.

But once, I think it was May morn,
    A stranger came along,
While Lucy milked, and sadly sung
    Her mother's little song.

He called her master to the road,
    And told him he would pay
Six hundred dollars for that girl,
    And take her right away.

Her master took the trader's gold;
    Such wicked things they do;
Just like a calf was Lucy sold,
    Though she was good as you.

Tom heard her scream, and ran
    to her;—
To part they could not bear;
He held her fast, and cursed
    the men,
Who stood in wonder there.

They knocked him down, and
    roughly took
Poor Lucy far away;
And toiling in some cotton field
    She weeps, perhaps, to-day.

Tom ran away, but dogs and men
    Were set upon his track,
And broken-hearted from
    the swamp
They brought him quickly back.

And then, 'twas said, they sold
    him off,
All chained, to Georgia men;
He may be dead, I never heard
    From that poor boy again.

JOHNNY VANLINE

Oh, never drink cider,
  Oh, never drink wine,
Nor beer, rum, nor brandy,
  Or shame will be thine.

Drink only cold water,
  And joy it will bring,
The clear, sparkling water
  That comes from the spring.

Young John loved the cider,
  And sucked through a straw
From the bung of a barrel,
  When no one he saw.

And when he was older,
  He drank beer, and wine;
A sot and a toper
  Was Johnny Vanline.

He lived near a tavern;
  And once he went there,
And he drank off some cordial
  And sat down in a chair.

Soon he called for some more,
  For it tasted so sweet,
And 'twas long after sunset,
  When he rose to his feet.

But he could not walk steady,
  And his brain gave a flutter,
And before he got home
  He fell down in the gutter.

Still he went for his dram
  To the tavern, each day,
Till he spent his last cent,
  And had nothing to pay.

His children were starving,
  But he beat them and swore,
And they trembled to see him
  Come in at the door.

But one cold, stormy night,
  He fell drunk by the sign
And they found him there dead:
  Poor Johnny Vanline !

Oh never drink cider,
  Oh never drink wine,
Nor beer, rum, nor brandy,
  Or shame will be thine.

Drink only cold water,
  And joy it will bring ;
The clear, sparkling water,
  That comes from the spring.

BASIL BROWN

"Give me that ball, I tell you now!"
  Cried angry Basil Brown,
And gave his school-mate
      such a push,
  As nearly threw him down.

He did not care how others felt,
  Nor seek to give them joy ;
For Basil only loved himself;
  He was a selfish boy.

He did not try, as good folks do,
  To keep his temper down;
A very over-bearing boy
  Was naughty Basil Brown.

One day, he tried to snatch a ball,
  As would often do,—
A ball his little brother had,
  Which Basil wanted too.

And when his brother held it fast,
  The angry Basil Brown
Then kicked him with his heavy boot,
  And knocked him quickly down.

He knocked him down, but
      never more
  He rose to play again;
He was so hurt that soon he died;
  And he was buried then.

Poor Basil could not eat for days,
  And hour by hour he'd weep;
He seemed to hear his brother scream
  When he would try to sleep.

Dear children, always try to keep
  Your rising temper down,
That you may never have to feel
  Like poor, poor, Basil Brown.

HENRY BOX BROWN

I will tell you the story of Henry Box Brown. It is a strange tale, and it is all true. Henry was a slave in Richmond, Virginia, and then his name was Henry Brown. He had a wife and four little children whom he loved very much.

One night when he went home to his little hut, his children and their mother were gone, and poor Henry found they had been sold to a trader, and were taken away to Carolina. It made him almost crazy to hear this dreadful news. He felt sure he should never see them again, for he was a slave, and would not be allowed to go after them. He had to work away for his master, just as if nothing had happened.

But he thought every day about his family, and he was very sad. He thought what hard times they would have when the overseer, with his whip, drove them to work in the cotton field. He feared they would have none to be kind to them, and love them; for the traders often sell the mother to one master, and the little children to others, and they never meet again. At last, Henry thought he would try to get to a free state. He resolved that, live or die, he would not be a slave much longer.

So he set to thinking how he should get off. He was afraid to run away, lest he should be caught and sent back. A slave is not allowed to travel without his master's leave. But he hit upon a lucky thought. He got a box just large enough to hold him when he was sitting down, with his head a little bent. The box was three feet long, two feet, eight inches deep, and twenty-three-and-a-half inches wide.

Then, he got a kind man to send word to a trusty friend in Philadelphia, that the box would be sent on the cars to Philadelphia, on a certain day. On the top of the box was written in large black letters, "this side up with care."

When it was nearly time for the cars to start, Henry took a bladder of water, some biscuit, and a large gimlet, and got into his box. Then a man nailed down the top, and porters took the box to the cars, thinking, I suppose, that it was a box of goods. It was very hot in the box, and Henry could hardly breathe, there was so little air. But he had made up his mind to die rather than make a noise, for then he would be found out, and sent back into slavery.

Part of the way, he travelled by water, and when the box was put on the steamboat, it was placed so that Henry's head and back were down; but he heard people moving about, and he feared they would hear him

if he turned; so he kept quite still. He lay in this way, while the boat went twenty miles, and it nearly killed him; he said the veins in his temples were great ridges that felt as big as his finger.

While Henry was lying with his head down, some men came and sat on the box, and he thought he heard one of them wonder what was in it.

He staid in his little box-house twenty-six hours; but he could not eat any of his biscuit, and instead of drinking the water, he used it to bathe his hot face. Most likely, he would have died if he had not bathed his face with the water. There he sat in the dark, sometimes fanning himself with his hat; and four times he bored a hole with the gimlet, to let in a little fresh air.

At last, on nearly the last day of March, 1849, the cars stopped in Philadelphia, and soon Henry felt the porters carrying him to the house of the kind man who was to receive him. The man shut the street door when the porters were gone, but he was afraid Henry was smothered, so he tapped with his fingers on the top of the box and asked, "all right?"

"All right, sir," said a voice in the box. Quickly the top of the box was knocked off, and Henry stood up. He shook hands with his new friend, and he was so happy that he hardly knew what to do.

After he had bathed himself and ate breakfast, he sang a hymn of praise, which he had kept in his mind to sing if he should ever get to a land of freedom in safety. The first lines were,

"I waited patiently for the Lord
And He inclined and heard me."

Henry was a strong, fine looking man. He was named Henry Box Brown, because he came nearly three hundred miles in a box. We call people heroes who do something that is brave and great, and Henry is a hero. Every body but the slaveholders seems glad of his escape from slavery. Henry will be well off in the free states, but his heart will always ache when he thinks of his wife and dear children. No one in Carolina is allowed to teach a slave to read or write; so he will never get a letter from any of his family, and it is not likely they will hear from him, or ever know that he is free.

LOLA LAKE
and LILA LEE

I'm going now to tell about
  Pale little Lola Lake,
Who teazed her mamma,
    every day,
For candy, nuts, and cake.

She loved her sweetmeats more
    than books,
  And more than work or play;
I cannot tell how many times
  She ate them every day.

At last her cheeks grew very pale,
  Her teeth began to ache,
And all because she lived so much
  On candy, tarts, and cake.

Dear Lila Lee grew strong
    and bright
  On plain and wholesome food,
She would not eat unhealthy things
  Because they tasted good.

It was a shame, she said, to do
  Like little Lola Lake :
And very seldom would she taste
  The candy or the cake.

She loved to help her mother work,
  And many books had she,
And all her brothers loved to read
  And play, with Lila Lee.

She often, with her pennies, bought
  An orange large and bright,
And took it to a poor, sick man
  Whose name was Billy Blight.

And when he heard her gentle step,
  And looked on Lila Lee,
He blessed the child, and said,
    "you are
  An angel sent to me."

And Lila, then, was happier far
  Than little Lola Lake,
And had more joy than if she'd
    bought
  Herself the nicest cake.

I'LL NEVER USE TOBACCO

"I'll never use tobacco, no!
 It is a nasty weed!
I'll never put it in my mouth:"
 Said little Robert Reid.

"Why there was idle Jerry James,
 As dirty as a pig,
Who smoked when only ten years old;
 And thought it made him big.

He'd puff along the open street
 As if he had no shame,
He'd sit beside the tavern door,
 And there he'd do the same.

He spent his time and money too,
 And made his mother sad;
She feared a worthless man would come
 From such a worthless lad.

Oh no ! I'll never smoke or chew,
 'T is very wrong indeed:
It hurts the health, it makes bad breath:"
 Said little Robert Reid.

THE CHESTNUT HUNT

Henry Sedgmoor and his sister Fanny had fine times in October, hunting chestnuts. Before it was fairly light in the morning, they were off to the trees to pick up the nuts which the wind had blown down in the night; and many a race they had with their young cousins to see who should be first at the tree.

But they all wanted the others to get a share of the nuts, and so they had no quarrels about them. Henry was sorry to see the sun rise when he was at the tree, for then he must hurry home to bring the cows. You could hear him almost half a mile as he went over the fields, calling, "Sukey, Sukey, Su, Su," at the top of his voice.

One night the children were in high spirits, for William, who was a man, had promised to go with them the next morning to whip the great chestnut tree, which they called "Big Brighty," because the nuts which grew on it were so large and bright. Their father said he would bring the cows for Henry that morning. Fanny asked her mother if Mary Ann, the little colored girl, might not go along, and her mother said "Yes, to be sure."

Little George, who was only five years old, had no notion of being left behind; and he hunted up his little tin cup, ready for an early start. His mother said they must mind and keep him from under the trees while the burrs were falling.

By the break of day, she heard them running past her window at full speed. Fanny and Henry each took one of little George's hands to help him along. Henry took the half peck, Fanny the little tin kettle, and Mary Ann the old school basket, and a great ringing and rattling they made as they went.

William cut a long pole and climbed almost to the top of the tree, and began to strike away. "Any coming?" he called down to the children.

"Yes, yes, they're rattling down like hail," they all answered.

"Take care the burrs don't fall on you," shouted William.

"I don't care for burrs," said Henry. But just then a great stinging burr fell on his hand, and he concluded it would be wiser to leave picking up the nuts till William went to another part of the tree.

Then such a bustling time as they had. Drop, drop, went the chesnuts into basket, kettle, and tin. They would shake the nuts as they passed one another, and say, "look what I've got;" and once Henry gave so hard a shake that part of his "shiners" flew out, and he had to pick them up again.

When William came down, they all wanted him to take a share of the nuts for whipping the tree; but he said "no no, keep them," and went home. At last, the chestnuts were all picked up. Henry had his half peck and pockets full, besides a large heap on the ground. He was, at first, puzzled how to carry all away, but he soon hit on a capital plan. He took off his coat and tied the ends of the sleeves with his garters, and then filled them with chestnuts.

"Why, Henry, you'll spoil your coat," said Fanny.

"Oh, its only my old one," answered Henry. The girls laughed at the odd figure he made, as he trudged home, carrying the peck in his arms, with his coat slung over his shoulder, and its long stiff arms dangling down. Little George had both his pockets swelled out to a great size, with chestnuts, and Mary Ann said he put her in mind of a ground squirrel with a chestnut in each side of its mouth. They sat down their loads and stopped awhile on the hill side to rest.

Henry took some nuts in his hand, and shutting it said, "hull gull."

"Hand full," said Fanny.

"Parcel how many?" said Henry.

"Ten," answered Fanny. Henry opened his hand, and there were only four. "Give me six to make it ten," said he.

Then Mary Ann took some chestnuts in one hand, and shutting both, held them up saying,

Niminy, niminy nake!
Which hand will you take?

"The left," said Fanny. Mary Ann opened her hands and the chestnuts were in the left, and so Fanny won that time. They played awhile, and Henry won the most nuts, but he gave them all back to the girls. "I only played for the fun of it," said he, "and I don't think it is a fair way of earning the chestnuts."

As they walked home they agreed that they would make a great boil for the whole family to eat that evening. Henry said, "I want some money, and must sell part of mine; but then I have almost half a bushel at home, and I mean to keep plenty to eat and give away in the winter."

Fanny said it was not wholesome to eat many chestnuts, and she would sell nearly all of hers, and buy a book and give to poor little Anabel Carey. She said Anabel's father was a drunkard, and her mother was poor, and so Anabel had no way to get nice books.

Mary Ann said she meant to sell her chestnuts and buy her father a handkerchief for a present, and the very next time she went home she would take it to him.

Little George asked Fanny if she thought he had enough chestnuts to buy a knife; and Fanny said when they got home they would fill up his little bag that hung up the chimney, and then he would have enough. Twice before they got home, the little fellow fell down and spilled all the nuts in his tin, but the children said "don't cry, Georgy," and soon picked them up for him.

It was after nine o'clock when they got home, and George ran ahead, and went straight to his mother to show his nuts, and said "Isn't there a heap?" The rest had much to tell her about their good luck, and they were all in such high spirits that they could scarcely eat their breakfast, though it had been waiting for them two hours.

THE EVENING HYMN
Little Alice Sings

My work is done, I've quit my play,
I'm older, now, another day,
And I will sing, before I rest,
This little hymn I love the best :
I will not fear in darkness deep,
For God is with us in our sleep,
And He will keep me, day and night,
Safe in His love if I do right.
When I'm alone, still near He'll be,
For, in my heart, He teaches me;
And I will try to do His will,
And, every day, grow better still.

About the Authors

Richard Beards, Ph. D., Editor has a B.A. from Dartmouth College and a Ph.D in English from the University of Washington, Seattle. He has taught at Temple University in Philadelphia since 1964, including courses in Victorian Studies and Children's Literature and Folklore. His experience also includes two teaching Fulbrights to Europe, one at Lund University, Sweden (1966-1967) and one at Odense University, Denmark (1971-1972). In 2008, Dr. Beards published an edition of Charles Kingsley's *Water Babies* for Penguin Classics. He is currently working on the 1842 diary of Lavinia Townsend, a Quaker Abolitionist active in Chester County, PA who travelled and recorded the words of Lucretia Mott, Frederick Douglass and other anti-slavery notables.

Stevie French, Illustrator & Designer graduated with honors from Virginia Commonwealth University in 2008. Her previous work includes writing and illustrating *Lizzie Fox-Top*, her first children's book, which received an honorable mention in the Writer's Digest International Self-Published Book Awards. When not making books, Stevie teaches art to children in Philadelphia, where she lives in a colorful apartment with a cat named Diego.

About the Publisher

For over 350 years the Religious Society of Friends has been made up of individuals witnessing to the trans-formative power of following the Inner Light, the true Light that lighteth everyone who has come into the world. In publishing books by and about Quakers, and books that examine Quaker values, *Inner Light Books* hopes to expand the knowledge of and appreciation for the faith and practice of the Religious Society of Friends.

For more information about our publications visit our website, www.innerlightbooks.com or write:
Editor, Inner Light Books
54 Lapidge Street
San Francisco, CA 94110, USA

The original 1849 edition of *Cousin Ann's Stories for Children* was published in Philadelphia by J.M. McKim. It has been reprinted under right of public domain.

The fonts used in this book are Times New Roman, Carmencita, Old Style, Chipperfield & Bailey, and Unicorn.

The original source for this book was designed in InDesign. The illustrations were hand-drawn in black ink, then scanned at 600 dpi and digitally colored in Photoshop.

This book was printed by Lightning Source, Inc.

CPSIA information can be obtained
at www.ICGtesting.com
Printed in the USA
BVHW020435170321
602670BV00001B/1